The "Write"
Way To Read

Volume 2

by

Marcia Weinstein, Ph. D.

BOOK LAB PUBLISHERS PO Box 206, Ansonia Station   New York, NY 10023-0206

Published by

BOOK LAB PUBLISHERS
PO Box 206, Ansonia Station
New York, NY 10023-0206
Telephone: 212 874-5534 . 800 654-4081
Telefax: 212 874-3105
Email: BOOKLABpub@aol.com

The "Write" Way To Read, Volume 2
Book number: 2313 ISBN number: 87594-364-0
The "Write" Way To Read, Volume 2 Teacher's Guide
Book number 2314 ISBN 87594-365-9

Production

Text Design & Typography: Maurice Leon
Cover Design: Alacart Design, Ltd.
Art and Illustrations: Erika Siskind & Alacart Design, Ltd.

OVERVIEW

The "Write" Way to Read is a program for beginning readers and writers of all ages. It is based on principles of phonetic spelling and trains students to make sound/symbol connections and write them when dictated. Dictation is a time-honored method for teaching the reading and writing of a new language.

The goals of the program are two-fold:
- mastery of phonetic spelling and our sound/symbol system
- using writing (encoding) to reinforce decoding for reading

The expectation is that students will build their phonic reading skills at the same time as they learn to spell. This will lead to confidence that they have the tools for their own writing needs.

In *Volume I*, students learn to distinguish and write all the consonant, consonant digraph, short vowel sounds and word patterns. The lessons concentrate on beginning and ending consonant sounds and beginning and medial vowels. They also include lessons on consonant blends and an introduction to two-syllable words. Simple sight words are introduced throughout the book. Sentence dictation is begun almost immediately. This assures recognition that letters and sounds may be used for words but that words are used to create thoughts and sentences. (Sentences in the early stages are stilted because of the limitation of all structured programs.)

Volume 2 follows the same format. It continues with two and three pattern words with consistent spelling, long vowels and r-modified vowel patterns.

The program is designed to be taught to a whole class, a small group or to individual students. It is appropriate for anyone who has begun to learn to read and write. *The "Write" Way to Read* can be used alone and as a natural adjunct to any phonetic decoding program.

While English is considered one of the most difficult languages to learn to read and to spell, it is consistent more than 80% of the time and these consistencies can be taught. Later, when a student feels confident about what he or she has already learned, the inconsistencies will be accepted and integrated with little difficulty.

HOW TO USE THIS BOOK

The "Write" Way to Read program is very easy to use. Directions to be dictated to the students are stated simply and clearly at the top of each page along with the instructional purpose and directions to the teacher.

> • The purpose of the lesson is stated in parenthesis.
> • The directions to be dictated to the students are in italics and quotes.

A few minutes devoted to this program daily in a structured and "expected" way will enhance any reading or writing program.

This book contains specific instructions for the use of the program with exact and complete lesson dictations.

1.   The basis for this word-attack program is "patterning." A pattern is a group of letters beginning with a vowel that is repeated in many words. Examples of patterns are "at" in "bat" and "hat"; "ent" in "went" and "spent"; "ate" in "hate" and "eed" as in "speed." This approach, with its strong emphasis on vowel sounds, is the "open sesame" to unlocking single and multi-syllabic words. Vowel sounds appear to be the major stumbling block to decoding mastery and require much greater attention than generally has been allotted.

The two concepts basic to the method are:
> 1. Word attack focusing on the prior determination of the vowel sounds, rather than attacking a word from its initial sound.
> 2. Determining the pattern that will key the word.

Initial consonants can be valuable in helping to determine a word in context. But they are usually not enough if the reader does not have strong clues as to what will follow. The pattern (which is determined by the initial vowel sound) provides the needed key. Even multisyllabic words are easily decoded when we can automatically clue into the first pattern. Once the student knows the first pattern and understands the sentence context, the whole word follows automatically. For example, in the sentence, "The children ate all the candy," the initial consonant provides a clue to the last word. Is it cookies, cake, candy, custard, cupcakes, carrots, etc? If the consonant "c" and the pattern "an" are known, the beginning is "can" and the rest becomes apparent.

2. Explain to students that they will learn to spell by listening to the sounds in the words they hear. Before each lesson, call students to the board to demonstrate examples of each activity. Choose students you feel will be the most likely positive models.* Pre-teach all lessons in this way and continue to reinforce throughout the year.

3. Encourage students to look at you as you enunciate the sounds of each letter in an exaggerated way. This helps the beginner become familiar with the sound. Examples of patterns are "at" in "bat" and "hat"; "ent" in "went" and spent"; "ate" in "hate"; and "eed" in "speed."

---

*MODELING is the most effective way to help students understand what is required of them. In a sense, acting serves as a picture of what is expected as the teacher "thinks aloud" through the process he/she wants emulated. If it is possible to use an assistant before calling students to model it would be ideal.

4. Constantly instruct students to repeat everything aloud as they write.

5. Define all vocabulary. Don't assume prior knowledge of any word used in the program.

6.   Pacing of *The "Write" Way to Read* will depend on the level and the ability of the group. It may be anywhere from one lesson a day (which is recommended) with additional practice on paper if necessary, to a session in which you take students as far as they can go. Each session will require a structured segment of time for pre-teaching, modeling and dictation.

7. It is very important that the teacher repeat, correct, and encourage as students work. The teacher should offer continuous praise for accuracy and neatness. This will make it easier for the students to be forthcoming when help is needed and will help control individual and group problems. The teacher should immediately correct student's mistakes; if not, they are likely to be repeated. Corrections should be given helpfully. It is counterproductive to point out students' errors as "wrong."

8. Be sure to teach the language of instruction you will use throughout the program. i.e: What is a vowel, a consonant, a syllable, etc. The use of the terms "long" or "short" to describe vowels is for the teacher's use only. These terms are often confusing to learners and are not necessary.

9. Teaching long vowel spellings
    Teaching long vowels is much more difficult than short vowels despite the popular misconception. With short vowels, a sound is memorized for the letter and remains consistent. Long vowels can be spelled in several ways, using silent letters and requiring thought. Various systems use different terminologies to explain the silent E (or the silent second adjacent vowel) such as "magic E", "brother E', etc.* Determine one you prefer that you have encountered or used with a basal reader or independent phonics program that you believe your students will respond to (depending on their age and maturity) and stick with it. Pre-teach and drill the concept before beginning Page 6 and again before each new lesson and new vowel sound. The vowel spellings included in the program are:

long A:	a-e	ai	ay
long E:	ee	ea	e-e (rarely used, unlike the others)
long I:	i-e	ie	igh y (just explain igh and y as "crazy")
long O:	o-e	oe	oa old
long U:	u-e	ue	ui

There are other spellings for these sounds but they needn't be considered at this learning stage as those we have included make up the majority of long vowel sounds.

Explain that reading and spelling English is difficult because there aren't enough letters to make all the sounds we need. The vowels are the worst because they can have several different sounds spelled several different ways and students have to know which sounds vowels make in a word or they can't read it. They also have to know which letters are needed to write the sound. Say: "In Volume 1 you learned how to spell the first sound for each vowel (ă ĕ ĭ ŏ ŭ). Now you are

---

* I favor a fairly silly explanation of the difference between short and long vowels in which the vowels are considered brothers. When alone and shy they will not say their names. But when a "brother" is along (ae ee ie oa etc.), either next to them or separated by a "friend" letter they are less shy and will make their name sound.

going to learn to spell the second sound – when a vowel says its name." Develop the chart and use many examples: ie.

      mad / made / maid   rid / ride   hop / hope   met / meet / meat   cute / cute

Drawing faces on the vowel letters on the board or making "brother vowel" dolls with reversible sides, facilitates the explanation and drill. "Magic E" works well when there is a vowel/consonant/vowel with a silent E. But it isn't useful when two vowels are together (ai ay ea oa ui). This requires another rule or explanation . The traditional "when two vowels go walking the first one does the talking" has many exceptions and needs to be explained away more often.

10, Teaching hard and soft C and G (Page 10)

    Drill the concept that C usually says "K." One must look to see what follows it. When followed by any letter, except and E, I or Y, it says "k." When followed by these letters, it says "s." (this is always true.) The same rule applies to G but there are several exceptions, such as "give" and "get.") You can chant "CE CI CY says "S" (GE GI GY says "J") and use numerous words as examples. i.e: cent city Nancy / gem ginger gym fudge

11.   Teaching R-modified vowel spellings

    Explain that there is a third sound that a vowel makes when it is followed by an R. AR = ar OR = or ER, IR, UR = er. Use whatever system you like for pre-teaching and just drill with flash cards, charts and games.

NOTES:

✔ In the instructions to the teacher letter names are written in capital letters. Lower case letters indicate the sounds of the letters.

✔ Teach and insist on punctuation marks in sentences.

✔ When pronouncing a word use the standard English pronunciation for the sample words for each vowel. Avoid the regional sound of 'dawg' for dog and keep 'jog,' 'hog,' 'log,' and 'dog.'

✔ When using examples of long vowel words don't 'throw any ringers' by using phonetically irregular words. These can be brought up during pre-teaching and explained: just point out if unexplainable or discuss at a later date. i.e: 'break' for long A (unexplainable) or the 'eh' sound of AE, as in 'head' and 'breath' (can be taught as a group.)

(Two syllable words with **er**)

*"Remember, when a pattern has two letters we have to double the ending consonant before we can make a longer word. Let's read the **er** patterns at the left side of the page together."*

"Now let's read the picture words together."

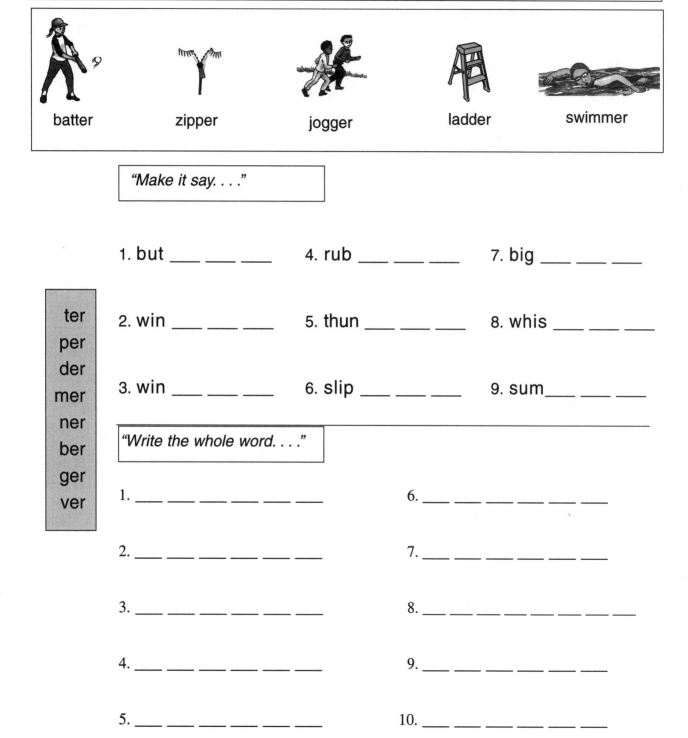

batter   zipper   jogger   ladder   swimmer

"Make it say. . . ."

ter	1. but ___ ___ ___ 4. rub ___ ___ ___ 7. big ___ ___ ___
per	
der	2. win ___ ___ ___ 5. thun ___ ___ ___ 8. whis ___ ___ ___
mer	
ner	3. win ___ ___ ___ 6. slip ___ ___ ___ 9. sum ___ ___ ___
ber	
ger	
ver	

"Write the whole word. . . ."

1. ___ ___ ___ ___ ___ ___   6. ___ ___ ___ ___ ___ ___

2. ___ ___ ___ ___ ___ ___   7. ___ ___ ___ ___ ___ ___

3. ___ ___ ___ ___ ___ ___   8. ___ ___ ___ ___ ___ ___ ___

4. ___ ___ ___ ___ ___ ___   9. ___ ___ ___ ___ ___ ___

5. ___ ___ ___ ___ ___ ___   10. ___ ___ ___ ___ ___ ___

(Two syllable words with **Y**)

"When a pattern has two letters we have to double the ending consonant before we can make a longer word. Let's read the picture word together."

puppy Jenny Tommy sunny happy

"Make it say. . . ."

1. pen ___ ___　　2. tum ___ ___　　3. hob ___ ___　　4. Pat ___ ___

"Write the whole word (name) . . . ."

1. ___ ___ ___ ___ ___　　3. ___ ___ ___ ___ ___　　5. ___ ___ ___ ___ ___

2. ___ ___ ___ ___ ___　　4. ___ ___ ___ ___ ___　　6. ___ ___ ___ ___ ___

"Write the sentence. . . ."

1. _____

_____

2. _____

_____

3. _____

_____

2

(Two syllable words with **et en est**)

"Let's read the picture words together."

puppet   kitten   thinnest   trumpet   fattest

"Make it say. . . ."

1. bon __ __ __   3. vel __ __ __   5. mit __ __ __   7. flat __ __ __

2. sud __ __ __   4. nug __ __ __   6. got __ __ __   8. wet __ __ __

"Write the whole word. . . ."

1. __ __ __ __ __ __

2. __ __ __ __ __ __

3. __ __ __ __ __ __ __

4. __ __ __ __ __ __

5. __ __ __ __ __ __

6. __ __ __ __ __ __

7. __ __ __ __ __ __

8. __ __ __ __ __ __

9. __ __ __ __ __ __ __ __

(Three syllable words with **ing er en** and **y**)

"Lets read he words together."

1. ham mer ing   3. stut ter ing   5. hap pen ing   7. flat ter ing

2. lot tery   4. sum mer y   6. win ter y   8. flat ter y

"Write the whole word. . . ."

1. _____   2. _____   3. _____   4. _____

3

(Teaching adding **"er"** to three- or four-pattern words)

"Let's read the picture word together."

| singer | thinker | jumper | faster | pitcher |

"Make it say. . . ."

1. long ___ ___   2. thrill ___ ___   3. catch ___ ___   4. bump ___ ___

"Next to number 1 write the word. . . ." (dust) *"Now write. . . ."* (duster) etc.

1. _____   3. _____   5. _____

   _____   _____   _____

2. _____   4. _____   6. _____

   _____   _____   _____

*"Just as we did when adding **ing** and **er** to words with two consonant patterns, we just add **y**, **et**, **en** and **est** the same way."*

"Make it say. . . ."

| **y** | **et** | **en** | **est** |

1. mess ___   4. pock ___   7. chick ___   10. long ___

2. luck ___   5. buck ___   8. kitch ___   11. fast ___

3. cand ___   6. crick ___   9. thick ___   14. strong ___

4

(Teaching past tense **ed**)

*"Just as with other little words, we double the last consonant before adding the **ed** unless there are already two consonants at the end. Then we can add the **ed**. Let's read the picture word together."*

clapped   hugged   batted   spilled   cracked

"Next to number 1 write the word. . . ." (slap)   *"Now write. . . ."* (slapped) etc.

1. _____   3. _____   5. _____

   _____   _____   _____

2. _____   4. _____   6. _____

   _____   _____   _____

'Write the sentence. . . ."

1. _____

   _____

2. _____

   _____

3. _____

   _____

(Introducing long **A** and long **A** patterns)

"*Say the pattern together. Now say the picture word and listen for the $\bar{a}$ pattern.
This is the first way to spell the $\bar{a}$ sound. Underline the pattern as you say the word.*"

ate	**ake**

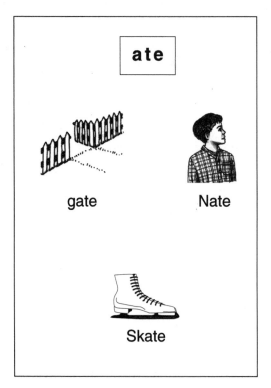

gate   Nate

Skate

cake   rake

lake

ame	**ave**

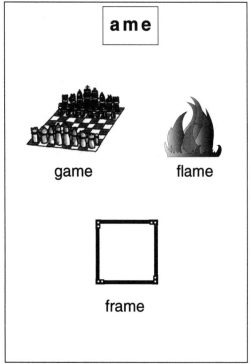

game   flame

frame

wave   Dave

shave

"Write the letter(s) to make it say. . . ."

1. ___ ate	6. ___ ake	11. ___ ame	16. ___ ave
2. ___ ate	7. ___ ake	12. ___ ame	17. ___ ave
3. ___ ate	8. ___ ake	13. ___ ame	18. ___ ave
4. ___ ___ ate	9. ___ ___ ake	14. ___ ___ ame	19. ___ ave
5. ___ ___ ate	10. ___ ___ ake	15. ___ ___ ame	20. ___ ___ ave

"Write the letter(s) to make it say. . . ."

1. m _____	4. d _____	7. st _____	10. qu _____
2. n _____	5. sh _____	8. fr _____	11. sh _____
3. g _____	6. bl _____	9. br _____	12. cr _____

(Making compound words)

"Put two words together. Write and say the new compound word."

1. cup cake _____   3. cave man _____

2. pan cake _____   4. milk shake _____

7

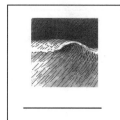

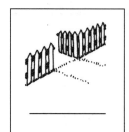

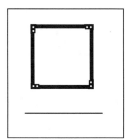

"Write the whole word. . . ."

1. _____   4. _____   7. _____   10. _____

2. _____   5. _____   8. _____   11. _____

3. _____   6. _____   9. _____   12. _____

*"Write the pattern I say. Decide if the sound of the letter **A** is ă or ā. Then decide if you need a silent **E** at the end to spell the pattern correctly."*

1. _____   3. _____   5. _____   7. _____

2. _____   4. _____   6. _____   8. _____

8

New Word | We   we | *"Write the sentences I say."*

1. _____

_____

2. _____

_____

3. _____

_____

4. _____

_____

5. _____

_____

6. _____

_____

"Say the pattern together. Now say the picture word and listen for the $\bar{a}$ pattern. Underline the pattern as you say the word."

ape

cape   tape

ane

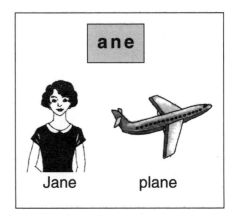

Jane   plane

ade

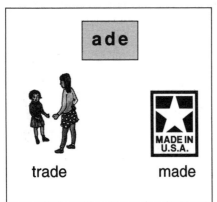

trade   made

ale

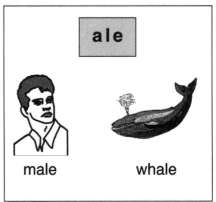

male   whale

ace

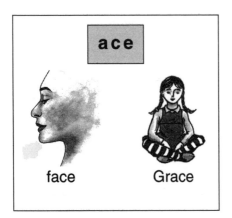

face   Grace

age

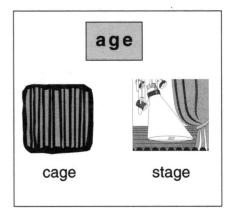

cage   stage

aze

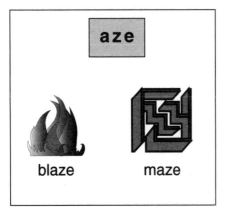

blaze   maze

are

share   mare

1. ____ ape   4. ____ ane   7. ____ ade   10. ____ aze

2. ____ ape   5. ____ ane   8. ____ ade   11. ____ aze

3. ____ ape   6. ____ ane   9. ____ ade   12. ____ aze

13. ____ ace   16. ____ age   19. ____ ale   22. ____ are

14. ____ ace   17. ____ age   20. ____ ale   23. ____ are

15. ____ ace   18. ____ age   21. ____ ale   24. ____ are

1. J _____   3. t r _____   5. s t _____   7. g r _____

2. w h _____   4. G r _____   6. g _____   8. p _____

1. _____   4. _____   7. _____   10. _____

2. _____   5. _____   8. _____   11. _____

3. _____   6. _____   9. _____   12. _____

New Word   **look   looks**   *"Write the sentences I say."*

_____

_____

_____

_____

_____

_____

_____

_____

_____

_____

_____

*"Listen to the **A** sound in the picture word I say. Decide if the **A** says ă or if it needs another vowel to make it say the ā sound. Then write the pattern to make it say the word. . . . Let's do the first set together."*

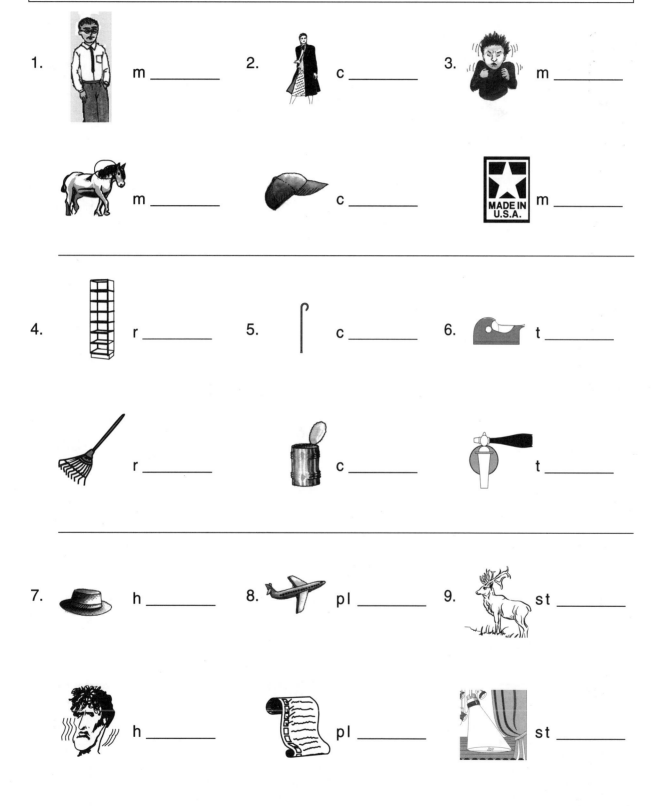

1. m _____

2. c _____

3. m _____

   m _____

   c _____

   m _____

4. r _____

5. c _____

6. t _____

   r _____

   c _____

   t _____

7. h _____

8. pl _____

9. st _____

   h _____

   pl _____

   st _____

(The **AI** spelling of long **A**)

"This is another way to spell the ā sound. Let's say the picture words together. Then underline the pattern as you say the word."

| wait | train | braid | sail | chair |

aid

paid
raid
maid
braid

ail

jail
mail
nail
sail
Gail
snail
trail
quail

aint

paint
quaint
saint

ait

bait
gait
wait

ain

pain
rain
main
brain
train
drain
chain
stain
plain
Spain

air

hair
pair
fair
chair
stair

"Write the letters you need to make it say. . . ."

1. ___ a i ___

2. ___ a i ___

3. ___ a i ___

4. ___ a i ___

5. ___ a i ___

6. ___ ___ a i ___

7. ___ ___ a i ___

8. ___ ___ a i ___

9. ___ a i ___ ___

10. ___ a i ___ ___

"Write the pattern to make it say. . . ."

1. w _____

2. ch _____

3. m _____

4. j _____

5. p _____

6. qu _____

7. st _____

8. pl _____

9. br _____

10. pa _____

14

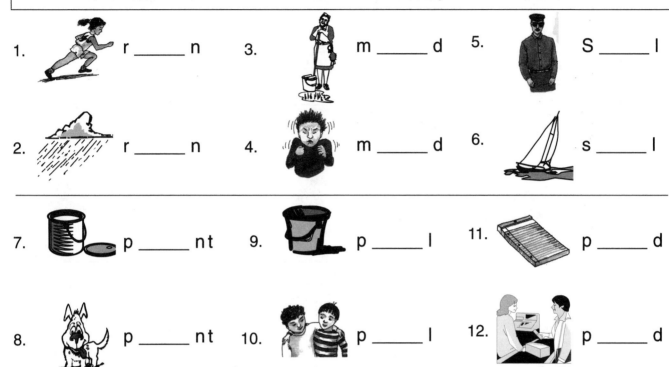

1. r _____ n

2. r _____ n

3. m _____ d

4. m _____ d

5. S _____ l

6. s _____ l

7. p _____ nt

8. p _____ nt

9. p _____ l

10. p _____ l

11. p _____ d

12. p _____ d

1._____   4. _____   7. _____

2._____   5. _____   8. _____

3._____   6. _____   9. _____

10._____   13. _____

11._____   14. _____

12._____   15. _____

New Word | **for** | *"Answer the questions in complete sentences."*

_____

_____

_____

_____

_____

_____

_____

_____

_____

_____

_____

_____

_____

(Adding second syllables to long vowel words when there is no silent **E** at the end.)

*"We learned that it is very easy to add a second syllable to words where two vowels come together to make the vowel's 'name' sound — like when **AI** says ā. Let's practice adding **ing**, **er**, **y** (ee) and **ed** to these words. Say them together."*

| raining | sailed | painter | fairy | waiter |

"Read the first word." (train) *"Now make it say what somebody is doing."* (training) etc.

What someone is doing.	t r a i n _____	What someone did.	w a i t _____
What someone did.	t r a i n _____	What someone is doing.	w a i t _____
The person doing it.	t r a i n _____	The person doing it.	w a i t _____
What it is doing.	r a i n _____	What someone did.	p a i n t _____
How it is.	r a i n _____	The person doing it.	p a i n t _____

"Write the whole word. . . ."

1. _____

2. _____

3. _____

4. _____

5. _____

6. _____

7. _____

8. _____

9. _____

10. _____

17

"Say the word   ***shake."***

*"Cross out the **E** and add **ing**."*   **s h a k e**   *"Write the word **shaking**."* _____

*"Cross out the **E** and add **er**."*   **s h a k e**   *"Write the word **shaker**."* _____

*"Cross out the **E** and add **y**."*   **s h a k e**   *"Write the word **shaky**."* _____

1. _____   5. _____   9. _____

2. _____   6. _____   10. _____

3. _____   7. _____   11. _____

4. _____   8. _____   12. _____

13. _____   17. _____   21. _____

14. _____   18. _____   22. _____

15. _____   19. _____   23. _____

16. _____   20. _____   24. _____

are   aren't   isn't

"Answer the questions in complete sentences."

1. Is Gail baking a cake?

   No, _____

   _____

2. Is it raining on the plain in Spain?

   Yes, _____

   _____

3. Is Jane waiting for the mailman at the mailbox?

   No, _____

   _____

4. Are the painters painting the trailer red?

   Yes, _____

   _____

5. Are Ted and Bobby going skating?

   No, _____

   _____

6. Did that fairytale scare you?

   Yes, _____

   _____

(Teaching the **AY** spelling for the long **A** sound)

"Look at the picture and try to read the words and the sentences to yourself. Then look at the list of words on the left side of the page and practice them with a partner. See if you can work out the hard words at the bottom."

playing

players

Bobby and Harry are playing.

"Write the letter(s) to make it say. . . ."

say
day
may
pay
hay
bay
jay
gay
way
ray
lay
play
clay
slay
stay
gray
pray
spray
tray
stray
sway

1. _____ a y   5. _____ a y i n g   9. _____ a y e r

2. _____ a y   6. _____ _____ a y i n g   10. _____ _____ a y e r

3. _____ _____ a y   7. _____ _____ a y i n g   11. _____ _____ a y e r

4. ___ ___ a y   8. ___ ___ ___ a y i n g   12. ___ ___ ___ a y e r

"Write the whole word. . ."

1. _____   5. _____   9. _____

2. _____   6. _____   10. _____

3. _____   7. _____   11. _____

4. _____   8. _____   12. _____

crayons
maybe
away
today
Sunday
Monday

"Fill in the blanks with one of the new words in the box. What you write must make sense."

1. My Mom is going _____ on a trip on _____.

2. I will be playing with my _____ _____.

3. _____ we can go fishing with you on _____.

"Say the pattern together. Now say the picture word and listen for the ē pattern.
This is the first way to spell the ē sound.   Underline the pattern as you say the word."

e e t

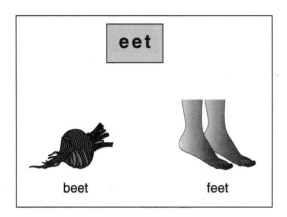

beet   feet

e e p

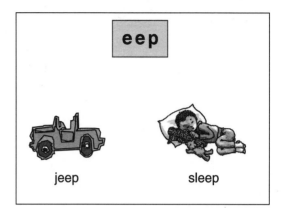

jeep   sleep

e e d

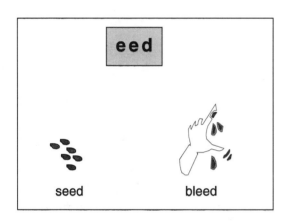

seed   bleed

e e k

cheek   peek

e e l

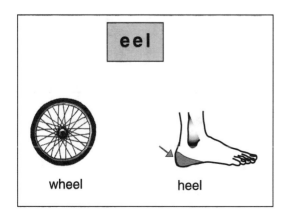

wheel   heel

e e r

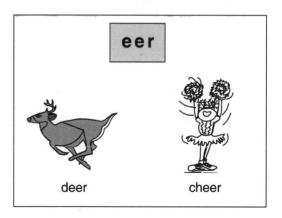

deer   cheer

(Initial consonants with long **E** patterns)

"Write the letter(s) to make it say. . . ."

1. ___e e t   3. ___e e l   5. ___e t e   7. ___e e p

2. ___ ___ e e t   4. ___ ___ e e l   6. ___ ___ e v e   8. ___ ___ e e p

---

9. ___e e k   11. ___e e n   13. ___e e r   15.___ ___ e e

10. ___ ___ e e k   12. ___ ___ e e n   14. ___ ___ e e r   16. ___ ___ ___ e e

"Write the pattern to make it say. . . ."

1. st_____   4. ch_____   7. j_____   10. s_____

2. wh_____   5. L_____   8. str_____   11. fl_____

3. sp_____   6. qu_____   9. sn_____   12. thr_____

"Write the whole word. . . ."

1. _____   3. _____   5. _____   7. _____

2. _____   4. _____   6. _____   8. _____

(Adding second syllables to long **E** words)

"Write the word. . . ." (meet) *"Now write. . . ."* (meeting)

1. _____   3. _____   5. _____   7. _____

2. _____   4. _____   6. _____   8. _____

9. _____   11. _____   13. _____   15. _____

10. _____   12. _____   14. _____   16. _____

*"Listen to the word and decide if it needs the ĕ or the ē vowel sound. Write the letter **E** if you hear the ĕ sound and 2 **Es** (**EE**) if you hear the ē sound."* (Do the first one together.) *"Make it say. . . ."*

1. m _____ t   3. ch ___ ___k   5. b ___ ___t   7. f ___ ll

2. m _____ t   4. ch ___ ck   6. b ___ t   8. f ___ ___ l

9. t _____ n   11. f ___ ___ d   13. p ___ ___ p   15. sp ___ d

10. t _____ n   12. f ___ d   14. p ___ p   16. sp ___ ___ d

"Write the sentences I say."

_____

_____

_____

_____

_____

_____

_____

_____

_____

_____

"This is another way to spell the ē sound. Let's say the picture words together. Underline the pattern as you say the word."

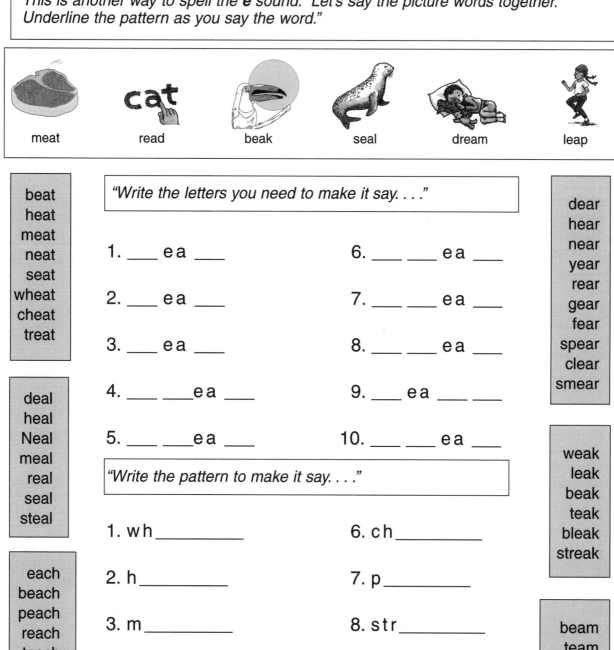

meat	read	beak	seal	dream	leap

beat
heat
meat
neat
seat
wheat
cheat
treat

deal
heal
Neal
meal
real
seal
steal

each
beach
peach
reach
teach
bleach

Jean
mean
lean
clean

dear
hear
near
year
rear
gear
fear
spear
clear
smear

weak
leak
beak
teak
bleak
streak

beam
team
seam
cream
dream
stream
scream
gleam

"Write the letters you need to make it say. . . ."

1. ___ e a ___   6. ___ ___ e a ___

2. ___ e a ___   7. ___ ___ e a ___

3. ___ e a ___   8. ___ ___ e a ___

4. ___ ___ e a ___   9. ___ e a ___ ___

5. ___ ___ e a ___   10. ___ ___ e a ___

"Write the pattern to make it say. . . ."

1. w h _____   6. c h _____

2. h _____   7. p _____

3. m _____   8. s t r _____

4. l _____   9. y _____

5. c r _____   10. J _____

(Some other words with ē patterns)

ease	east	geese	sleeve	breeze
tease	beast	cheese	leave	freeze
please	least			sneeze

25

1. b ___ t   3. b ____ d   5. sp ___ ___ k   7. s ___ ___ l   9. m ____ n

2. b ___ ___ t   4. b ___ ___ d   6. sp ____ k   8. s ____ ll   10. m ___ ___ n

"Next to the number 1. write the word. . . ."
"Next to the number 2. write the word. . . ."
"Next to the number 3. write the word. . . ."

1. _____   4. _____   7. _____   10. _____

2. _____   5. _____   8. _____   11. _____

3. _____   6. _____   9. _____   12. _____

"Chose a word that makes sense in the sentence. Circle the word and fill in the blank."

Example: Did Steve <u>beat</u> you at chess?   a. bet / beet / (beat)

1. Did Eve _____ Fred last week?
   a.

2. Yes, she _____ him on Beech Street.
   b.

3. That chicken is going to _____ at my feet.
   c.

4. I am going to _____ in the box to see my gift.
   d.

5. For dinner we will eat _____, _____ and
   e.   f.
   _____.
   g.

6. I see a _____ of dust on that _____.
   h.   i.

a. met / meet / meat

b. met / meet / meat

c. peck / peek / peak

d. peck / peek / peak

e. met / meet / meat
f. ben / been / beans
g. bet / beets / beat

h. speck / speek / speak
i. set / seet / seat

26

(Adding second syllables to **EA** words)

*"Remember when you add a second syllable to **EA** patterns you don't have to change anything. Just add **ing**, **er**, **y**, **ed** or **en**."*

"Next to the number 1 write the word. . . ." (beat)
"Next to the number 1 write the word. . . ." (beating) etc.

1. _____

2. _____

3. _____

4. _____

5. _____

6. _____

7. _____

8. _____

9. _____

10. _____

11. _____

12. _____

13. _____

14. _____

15. _____

16. _____

17. _____

18. _____

19. _____

20. _____

21. _____

22. _____

23. _____

24. _____

"Write the sentences I say."

(Introducing long **I** and long **I** patterns)

*"Say the new **I** patterns together. Now say the picture word and listen for the pattern. This is the first way to spell the **i** sound. Underline the pattern as you say the word."*

ie

tie

pie

i-e

bite

ride

igh

high

night

ire

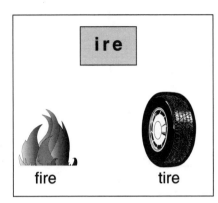

fire   tire

ive

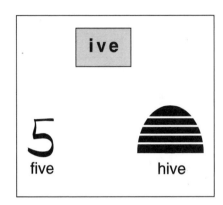

five   hive

ice

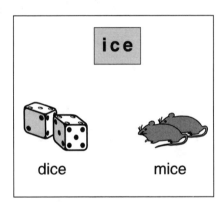

dice   mice

ike

bike   Mike

ide

hide   bride

ime

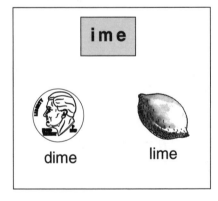

dime   lime

ine

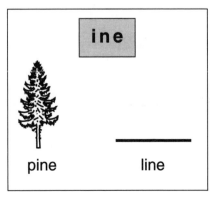

pine   line

ile

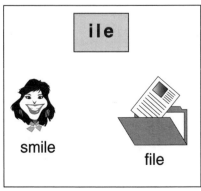

smile   file

1. ___ i p e   3. ___ i t e   5. ___ i l e   7. ___ i r e

2. ___ ___ i p e   4. ___ ___ i t e   6. ___ ___ i l e   8. ___ i r e

---

9. ___ i n e   11. ___ i v e   13. ___ i e   15. ___ i c e

10. ___ ___ i n e   12. ___ ___ i v e   14. ___ ___ i e d 16. ___ ___ i c e

"Write the pattern to make it say. . . ."

1. l _____   4. t w _____   7. w _____   10. q u _____

2. w _____   5. s p _____   8. d _____   11. s t r _____

3. c r _____   6. w h _____   9. l _____   12 . t r _____

"Write the whole word. . . ."

1. _____   3. _____   5. _____   7. _____

2. _____   4. _____   6. _____   8. _____

30

"Say the word   **s h i n e** *."*

*"Cross out the **E** and add **ing**."*   **s h i n e**   *"Write the word shining."* _____

*"Cross out the **E** and add **y**."*   **s h i n e**   *"Write the word shiny."* _____

*"Cross out the **E** and add **ed**."*   **s h i n e**   *"Write the word shined."* _____

"Now do it yourself.
"Next to number 1 write the word. . . ." (hike)
"Next to number 2 write the word. . . ." (hiking) etc.

1. _____   4. _____   7. _____

2. _____   5. _____   8. _____

3. _____   6. _____   9. _____

10. _____   13. _____   16. _____

11. _____   14. _____   17. _____

12. _____   15. _____   18. _____

"Answer the questions in complete sentences."

1. Do you like ice cream?

   Yes, _____

   _____

2. Is Mike going to eat a slice of pie?

   No, _____

   _____

3. Is it fun to play hide and seek?

   Yes, _____

   _____

4. Do you think mice are nice?

   No, _____

   _____

5. Is it better to ride a bike or take a hike?

   _____

   _____

(Teaching the **igh** and **y** spellings of long **I**)

"IGH and Y are the other usual ways to spell the ī sound. Let's say the picture words together. Underline the pattern as you say the word."

| night | light | fight | fright | cry |

"Write the letter(s) to make it say. . . ."

fight		my
night	1. ___ i g h	by
right		why
sight	2. ___ i g h	fly
tight		sly
might	3. ___ i g h t	cry
light		dry
flight	4. ___ i g h t	fry
slight		try
brigh	5. ___ ___ i g h t	sky
t		spy
		shy
		spry

1. ___ i g h   6. ___ ___ i g h t

2. ___ i g h   7. ___ ___ i g h t

3. ___ i g h t   8. ___ ___ i g h t

4. ___ i g h t   9. ___ ___ y

5. ___ ___ i g h t   10. ___ ___ y

"Write the whole word. . . ."

| high |
| sigh |
| thigh |

1. _____   5. _____   9. _____

2. _____   6. _____   10. _____

3. _____   7. _____   11. _____

4. _____   8. _____   12. _____

33

(Adding second syllables to words spelled with **IGH** and **Y**)

"Make it say. . . ."

1. cry _____

2. high _____

3. sigh _____

4. fight_____

5. might_____

6. fright_____

7. bright_____

8. light_____

9. tight_____

"Write the whole word. . . ."

1. _____

2. _____

3. _____

4. _____

5. _____

6. _____

7. _____

8. _____

9. _____

10. _____

11. _____

12. _____

13. _____

14. _____

15. _____

16. _____

"Do you think you can read three syllable words? Try these."

1. t i g h t e n i n g   2. f r i g h t e n i n g   3. b r i g h t e n i n g

"Now cover the words and try to write them."

1. _____   2. _____   3. _____

34

(Adding **ly** to form adverbs) There is never a change, we just add the **ly**.

"Next to number 1 write the word. . . ." (glad)
"Next to number 2 write the word. . . ." (gladly) etc.

1. _____   3. _____   5. _____   7. _____

(More three-pattern words)

"Next to number 1 write the word (or the syllable). . . ." (but)
"Next to number 2 write the word. . . ." (butter) *"Now write. . . ."* (buttering) etc.

1. _____   6. _____   11. _____

2. _____   7. _____   12. _____

3. _____   8. _____   13. _____

4. _____   9. _____   14.

5. _____   10. _____

15. _____   19. _____   23. _____

16. _____   20. _____   24. _____

17. _____   21. _____   25. _____

18._____   22. _____   26. _____

"Write the sentences I say."

(Introducing long **O** and long O patterns)

*"Say the new **O** patterns together. Now say the picture word and listen for the ō pattern. This is the first way to spell the ō sound. Underline the pattern as you say the word."*

oe

toe

toes

o-e

joke

hope

oa

boat

toast

old

cold

told

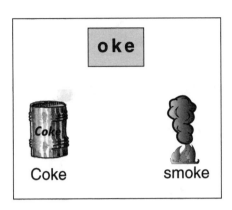

oke

Coke

smoke

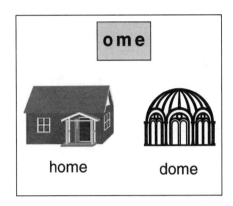

ome

home

dome

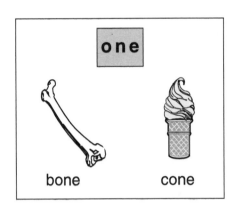

one

bone

cone

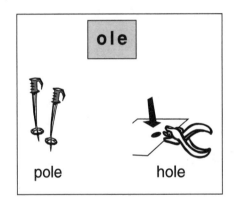

ole

pole

hole

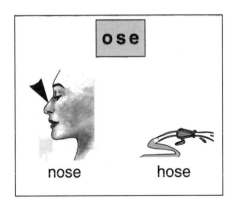

ose

nose

hose

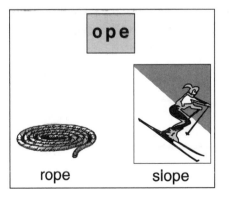

ope

rope

slope

1. ____ o b e   3. ____ o n e   5. ___ ___ o s e   7. ____ o l e

2. ___ ___ ___ o b e 4. ___ o n e   6. ___ ___ o s e   8. ____ o l e

9. ____ o k e   11. ___ ___ o r e   13. ___ ___ o v e   15. ____ o m e

10. ___ ___ o k e   12. ___ ___ o r e   14. ___ ___ o v e   16. ___ o m e

1. r _____   4. fr_____   7. s l _____   10. q u _____

2. b r _____   5. R_____   8. c h _____   11. c _____

3. p _____   6. s t _____   9. s t _____   12 . c h _____

1. _____   4. _____   7. _____

2. _____   5. _____   8. _____

3. _____   6. _____   9. _____

38

(Teaching the **OA** spelling of the long **O** sound)

"This is another way to spell the ō sound. Let's say the picture words together. Listen to the patterns you hear in these words. Underline the pattern as you say the word."

 toad  cloak   loaf  soap  boat

oad
road
toad
load

oak
soak
cloak
croak

oat
boat
coat
goat
moat
float
gloat
throat

oach
coach
roach
poach

oal
coal
goal
foal

oar
roar
boar
soar

oan
Joan
loan
moan
groa

oast
boast
toast
coast

oam
foam
roam

"Write the letters you need to make it say. . . ."

1. __ __ o a __   6. __ o a __

2. __ o a __   7. __ o a __

3. __ __ o a __   8. __ o a __

4. __ o a __   9. __ o a __

5. __ o a __ __   10. __ o a __ __

"Write the pattern to make it say. . . ."

1. g r _____   6. t _____

2. c r _____   7. s _____

3. r _____   8. r _____

4. t h r _____   9. f _____

5. g _____   10. c _____

39

1. c_____ t   3. r_____ d   5. s_____ c k   7. c_____ s t   9. c l_____ c k

2. c_____ t   4. r_____ d   6. s_____ k   8. c_____ s t   10. c l

old
fold
cold
hold
told
gold
mold
sold
bold
scold

1. __ o l d   2. __ o l d   3. __ o l d   4. __ o l d   5. __ __ o l d

"Write the whole word. . ."

1. _____   3. _____   5. _____   7. _____

2. _____   4. _____   6. _____   8. _____

(Adding second syllables to long **O** words)				
Examples: vote	toast	old	lone	close
voter	toasted	older	lonely	closely
voted	toaster	olden		
voting	toasting	oldy		

"Read the first word." (fold) *Now make it say what someone is doing."* (folding) etc.

f o l d

What someone is doing. _____

What someone did. _____

What we keep papers in. _____

j o k e

What someone did. _____

What someone is doing. _____

The person doing it. _____

t o a s t

What someone is doing. _____

What we use to do it. _____

When it is nice and warm it is _____

p o k e

What someone did. _____

What someone is doing. _____

What we use to do it. _____

"Next to number 1 write the word. . ." (scold)
"Next to number 2 write the word. . ." (scolding) etc.

1. _____   4. _____   7. _____

2. _____   5. _____   8. _____

3. _____   6. _____   9. _____

1. I ate a very _cold_ ice cream _____.
   a.   b.

a soapy	b. loaf
code	cone
(cold)	cope

2. Joe's _____ and toes _____ from the icy cold .
   a.   b.

a. nose	b. hoped
rose	goes
notes	froze

3. My _____can_____ on the pond.
   a.   b.

a. bone	b. float
boat	load
bed	lap

4. Joan got a bad _____ and a sore _____.
   a.   b.

a. coke	b. stone
coat	throat
cold	neck

5. Rose _____a green dress and a red hat.
   a.

a. closed
chose
likes

6. Please _____ the lid on the box.
   a.

a. close
chose
quit

7. Moses rode his bike on the _____ near the sea _____.
   a.   b.

a. rope	b. store
street	shore
road	shell

8. I hope I can go _____ today.
   a.

a. swimming
home
fishing

9. My dad _____ home from the store.
   a.

a. floated
drive
drove

10. I'm feeling very _____ and I'm _____ my
    a.   b.
    mom will not be home late.

a. lonely	b. hopping
broken	hoping
sad	seeing

42

"Read the first word. Then change one letter, or add or take away a silent **E** to make it say the new word. . . . Write the word on the next line."

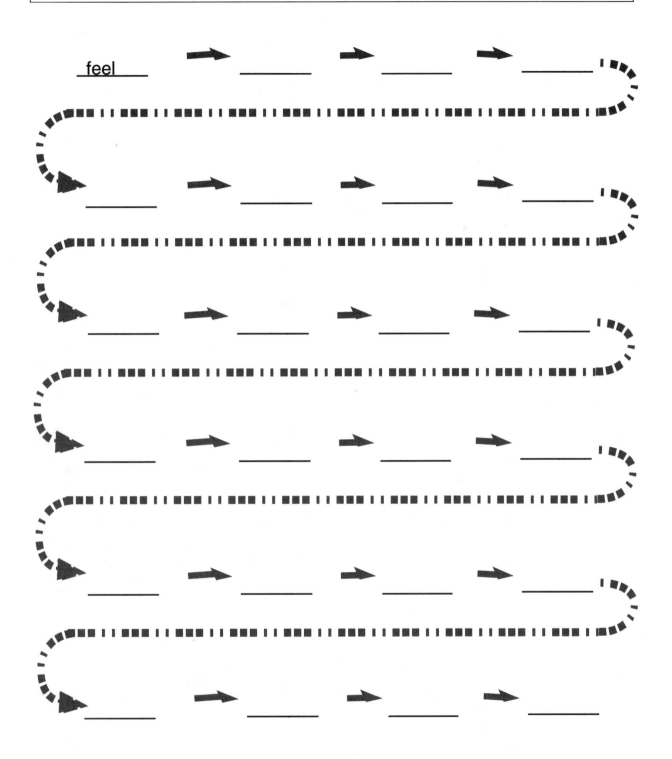

feel

1. _____

2. _____

3. _____

4. _____

5. _____

6. _____

7. _____

8. _____

9. _____

10. _____

11. _____

12. _____

13. _____

14. _____

15. _____

16. _____

17. _____

18. _____

19. _____

20. _____

21. _____

22. _____

23. _____

24. _____

25. _____

26. _____

27. _____

28. _____

29. _____

30. _____

31. _____

32. _____

33. _____

34. _____

35. _____

36. _____

37. _____

38. _____

39. _____

40. _____

(Introducing long **U** and long **U** patterns (**u e**   **u - e**   **u i**)

*"Say the new **U** patterns together. Then say the picture words and listen for the patterns."*

u t e

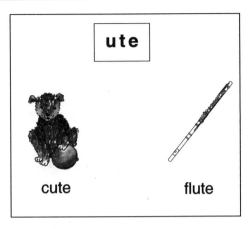

cute   flute

u b e

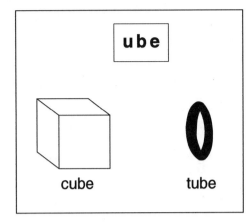

cube   tube

u l e

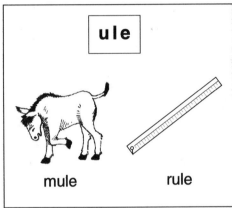

mule   rule

u n e

June   tune

u e

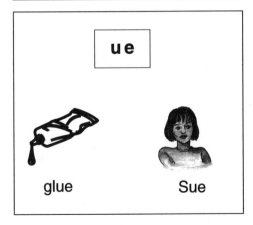

glue   Sue

u i t

suit   fruit

uke	uce	uice	uise	uel	uge
Duke	truce	juice	bruise	fuel	huge
Luke	Bruce		cruise	cruel	

45

1. ____ u t e

3. ____ u b e

5. ____ u s e

7. ____ ____ u e

2. ____ ____ u t e

4. ____ u b e

6. ____ u s e

8. ____ ____ u e

9. ____ u n e

11. ____ u l e

13. ____ u i t

15. ____ u d e

10. ____ u n e

12. ____ u l e

14. ____ ____ u i t

16. ____ u d e

1. b r _____

3. f _____

5. r _____

7. J _____

9. f r _____

1. _____

3. _____

5. _____

7. _____

9. _____

2. _____

4. _____

6. _____

8. _____

10. _____

46

u s e

What someone did. _____

The person doing it. _____

What someone is doing. _____

r u l e

What someone is doing. _____

What they are using to do it. _____

What someone did. _____

---

t u n e

What someone did. _____

What someone is doing. _____

The person doing it. _____

b r u i s e

What someone did. _____

What someone is doing. _____

The person doing it. _____

1. t _____   3. c _____   5. f _____   7. p l _____   9. _____

2. t _____   4. c _____   6. f _____   8. p l _____   10. _____

---

11. d _____   13. c _____   15. d _____   17. L _____   19. m _____

12. d _____   14. c _____   16. d _____   18. l _____   20. m _____

New Word | **Can't** | *"Answer the questions in complete sentences."*

1. Can Bruce play the flute?

   No, _____

   _____

2. Do you think that fuzzy mutt is very cute?

   Yes, _____

   _____

3. Can you use glue to fix the broken ruler?

   No, _____

   _____

4. Can Sue bring ice cubes for the grapefruit juice?

   Yes, _____

   _____

5. Did Luke get bruised in his fight with The Duke?

   Yes,_____

   _____

6. Are you and dad using fuses to fix the lights?

   No, _____

   _____

48

"Read the first word. Then change one letter, or add or take away a silent **E** to make it say the new word. . . . Write the word on the next line."

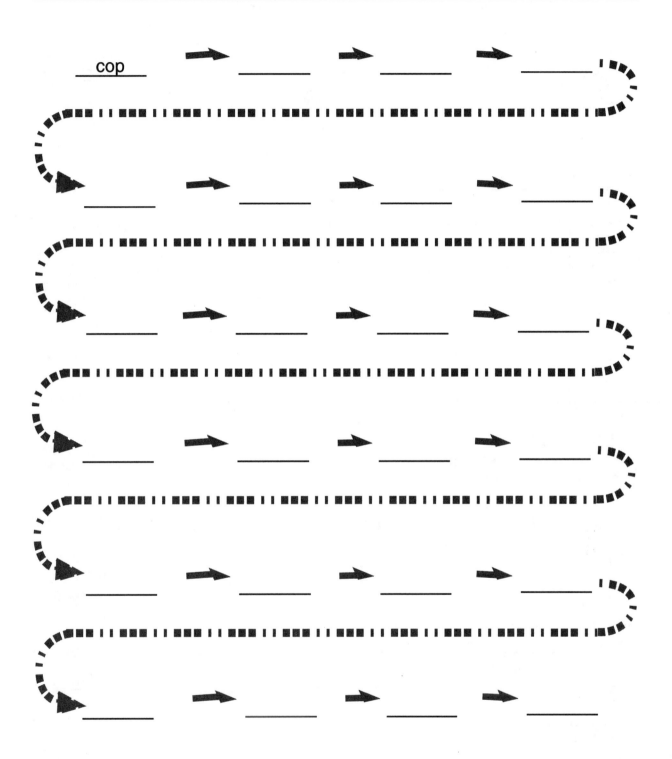

(Introducing **R-modified** vowels and patterns – the **är** sound of **AR**)

*"Let's say the picture words together. Listen for the **är** sound that is the usual sound when **A** and **R** are together. Underline the pattern as you say the word."*

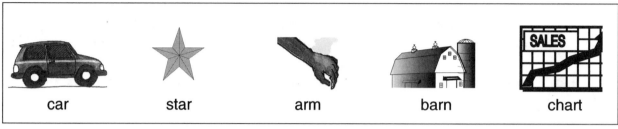

car	star	arm	barn	chart

---

car	*"Write the letter(s) you need to make it say. . ."*		art
far			part
jar	1. ___ a r	5. ___ ___ a r ___	9. ___a r ___	dart
bar			chart
star			smart
scar	2. ___a r ___	6. ___ a r ___ ___	10. ___ ___ a r	start

arm	3. ___ ___ a r ___	7. ___ ___a r ___ ___	11. ___ a r ___ ___	barn
harm				yarn
farm				darn
charm	4. ___ a r ___	8. ___ a r ___ ___	12. ___ ___ a r ___	
warm				
swarm	*""Write the pattern . . . ."*		harp

park	1. f _____	4. s t _____	7. m _____	carp
bark				sharp
mark	2. y _____	5. s h _____	8. l _____	large
dark				barge
shark	3. s c _____	6. h _____	9. s h _____	charge
spark	*"Write the word. . . ."*		carve

hard				starve
yard	1. _____	3. _____	5. _____	arch
card				march
lard	2. _____	4. _____	6. _____	starch

50

1. _____   5. _____   9. _____

2. _____   6. _____   10. _____

3. _____   7. _____   11. _____

4. _____   8. _____   12. _____

"Do you think you can read these three syllable words?"

1. s h a r p e n e r   2. h a r d e n i n g   3. d a r k e n i n g

"Now cover the words and try to write them."

1. _____   2. _____   3. _____

(Putting together two known syllables to make new words)

Example: barn ⟍   ⟋ness   barnyard

⟍ ⟋

⟋ ⟍

dark ⟋   ⟍yard   darkness

"Match the syllables to make new words. Then write the words on the line."

dar   ther _____   car   ner _____

far   pet _____   gar   fare _____

mar   ling _____   part   chair _____

car   den _____   bar   bage _____

gar   ket _____   arm   ber _____

51

New Word | **Don't don't** | "Choose the one that makes sense in the sentence."

1. In squishy mud _____ feet feel nice.

bar bare

2. A _____ on my bike broke.

3. Martin got a gold _____ from his teacher.

star stare

4. Please don't _____ at me.

5. Thunder and lightening _____ me.

scar scare

6. I got a bad _____ on my arm.

7. Please don't go _____ away this time.

far fare

8. The train _____ is five dollars.

9. We can take a ride in the blue _____.

car care

10. I don't _____ for that suit.

"Write the sentences I say."

_____

_____

_____

_____

_____

_____

_____

_____

_____

_____

_____

(The **R-modified** sound of **O**)

*"Let's say the picture words together. Listen for the **ar** sound that is the usual sound which **O** and **R** are together. Underline the pattern as you say the word."*

fork   cord   horn   horse   store

"Write the letter(s) to make it say . ."

cork		born
fork	1. __ o r__ 4. __ o rse 7. __ __ o r__ 10. __ __ o r__	corn
pork		horn
york	2. __ __ or__ 5. __ __ ore 8. __ ore 11. __ or__ __	torn
stork		worn
	3. __ __ or__ 6. __ or__ 9. __ or__ 12. __ or__ __	thorn

"Write the pattern to make it say. . ."

port		wore
sort	1. st_____ 4. sc_____ 7. t_____ 10. w_____	tore
Mort		more
short	2. M_____ 5. c_____ 8. sh_____ 11. p_____	sore
sport		bore
	3. w_____ 6. st_____ 9. h_____ 12. f_____	shore
		chore
		snore
form	*"Can you put two syllables together to make a new word that fits into the sentence."*	score
storm		store

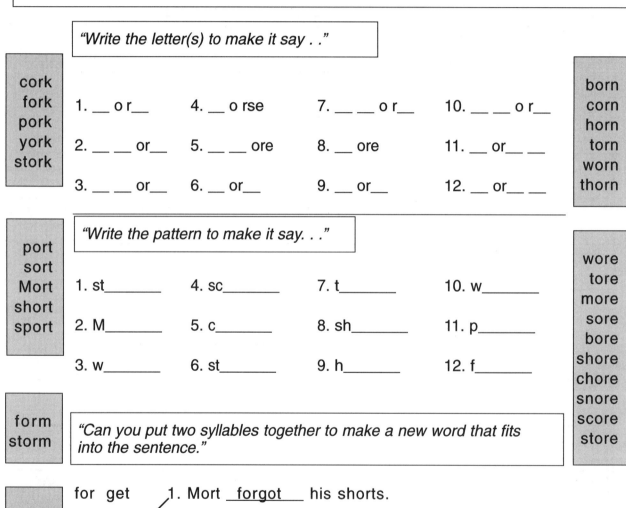

	for get	1. Mort __forgot__ his shorts.
porch		
torch	for got	2. We must go to the store _____ lunch.
scorch		
	for bid	3. My dad _____ me to go near the corner.
	be fore	4. I can't _____ that frightening story.
	ig nore	5. Please don't _____ me when I look at you.

54

Examples: score   form
              scoring   forming
              scored   formed

"Read the first sentence. How somebody is." (short) *"Now make it say 'but someone is. . .'"* (shorter) etc.

How somebody is. _short_____

But somebody _____ .

And who is the _____ .

What might we do to pants. _____

When we will leave. _____ .

short
shorten
shorter
shortest
shortly

When we make somebody do something we _____ them.

What we are doing to them. We are _____ them.

What we did to them. We _____ them.

The person doing it is the _____.

force
forced
enforcer
forcing

We are going to have a _storm_ .

Yesterday it also _____ .

It was very _____ .

It was _____ all day.

Some things _bore_____ me.

They are very _____ .

And I feel _____ .

"Write the sentences I say."

_____

_____

_____

_____

_____

_____

_____

_____

_____

_____

_____

_____

(Reviewing **er**, the **R** modified sound of **E**)

*"Let's say the picture words with the **er** sound together."*

| Bertha | Bert | fern | clerk |

"Can you read these words?"

1.Bert	3. term	5. jerk	7. fern	9. serve	11. perch
2. pert	4. germ	6. clerk	8. stern	10. nerve	12. verse

"Now see if you can write the letters to complete the word."

1. __ er __	4. __ er __ __	7. __ er __ __	10. __ er__
2. __ e r__	5. __ er __	8. __ __ er __	11. __ er __ __
3. __ er __	6. __ __ er __	9. __ er __	12. __ er __ __

"Can you put two syllables together to make a new word that fits into the sentence."

per son   1. A _____ is partly a fish and partly a girl.

ter mite   2. My teacher will not _____ messy work.

mer maid   3. That clerk is a very nice ____person____ .

per mit   4. A _____ is a very bad bug.

her self   5. Bertha can't play in the park by _____ .

(More practice with the **er** sound)

"Next to number 1 write the word. . ." (perch)
"Next to number 2 write the word. . ." (perched) etc.

1. _____   4. _____   7. _____

2. _____   5. _____   8. _____

3. _____   6. _____   9. _____

"Can you hear the different vowel sounds in the words 'batter' and 'bitter.' Listen to the vowel sound in the word I say. Fill in the blank with the letter that makes the sound."

1. b____ tter   3. s____ mmer   5. r____ bber   7. p____ pper   9. l____ tter

2. b____ tter   4. s____ mmer   6. r____ bber   8. p____ pper   10. l____ tter

"Put two syllables together and write the new word."

1. ser pent _serpent_   4. mer maid _____   7. per mit _____

2. ser vent _____   5. per son _____   8. her self _____

3. ter mite _____   6. her mit _____   9. per haps _____

"Answer YES, NO, or MAYBE."

1. Is a serpent a snake? _____   5. Can a person be perfect? _____

2. Is a servant a helper? _____   6. Is a termite a bug? _____

3. Is a mermaid real? _____   7. Can Fern dress herself? _____

4. Is 'perhaps' the same as 'maybe'? _____   8. Can Herman be a hermit? _____

58

(Introducing **ir**, the R-modified sound of **I**)

*"Let's say the picture words together. Listen for the **ir** sound that is the usual sound when **I** and **R** are together. Underline the pattern as you say the word."*

bird girls skirt birch Kirk

"Write the letters to make it say. . . ."

1. ___ ___ i r ___ 3. ___ ___ i r ___ 5. ___ i r ___ ___ 7. ___ i r ___

2. ___ ___ i r ___ 4. ___ i r ___ ___ 6. ___ ___ i r ___ 8. ___ ___ i r

---

"Write the pattern to make it say. . . ."

1. f_____ 3. fl_____ 5. w h_____ 7. sh_____

2. th_____ 4. b_____ 6. th _____ 8. squ_____

"Write the whole word. . ."

1. _____ 3. _____ 5. _____ 7. _____

2. _____ 4. _____ 6. _____ 8. _____

"Read the first sentence." (Birds can chirp.) "Now add a syllable to complete the sentence."

Birds can __chirp_____ .

The cheer leaders __twirl_____ .

They are _____ .

They are _____ .

Yesterday they _____ .

Yesterday they _____ .

Dick and Kirk __squirt____ the squirt gun.

Shirley likes to __flirt_____ .

They are _____ the gun.

She is _____ .

Yesterday they _____ the gun.

Yesterday she _____ .

"Match the words that have the same meaning."

Same   Different

whirl	Mister
thirteen	30
sir	twirl
dirty	13
thirty	messy

	Same	Different
dirty - clean	____	__✓__
whirl - twirl	____	____
first - last	____	____
chirp - sing	____	____
thirsty - hungry	____	____

"Write the sentences I say."

nurse   surf   church   purse   hurt

"Write the letter(s) to make it say. . . ."

1. ___ u r ___   3. ___ u r ___ ___   5. ___ u r ___ ___   7. ___ u r ___

2. ___ ur ___ ___   4. ___ ___ u r   6. ___ u r r   8. ___ u r ___ ___

"Write the pattern to make it say. . ."

1. t _____   3. b _____   5. h _____   7. l _____

2. c h _____   4. p _____   6. c _____   8. sp _____

"Make the whole word. . . ."

1. _____   3. _____   5. _____   7. _____

2. _____   4. _____   6. _____   8. _____

62

(Adding **le** to make a new second syllable to add to known words)

"Let's read these lists of words together. Then you will write some."

tle	**dle**	**ple**	**ble**	**kle**	**gle**	**zle**
bot tle	pud dle	ap ple	bub ble	an kle	tan gle	puz zle
lit tle	pad dle	sim ple	peb ble	tin kle	sin gle	daz zle
set tle	hur dle	tem ple	gob ble	spar kle	wig gle	siz zle
star tle	han dle	top ple	scrib ble	snor kle	jun gle	driz zle
tur tle	bun dle	pur ple	grum ble	sprin kle	strug gle	noz zle

"Make it say. . . ."

1. rat _____   3. mid _____   5. dim _____   7. gar _____

2. gig _____   4. nib _____   6. ket _____   8. spar _____

"Fill in the blank with AR. OR, ER, IR or OR."

1. ch ____ ____ t   6. sh ____ ____

2. p ____ ____ ch   7. wh ____ ____ l

3. b ____ ____ n   8. f ____ ____ ce

4. cl ____ ____ k   9. f ____ ____ st

5. st ____ ____ tle   10. p ____ ____ ple

1. Bert _____ on the burner on the stove.

2. Shirley was using _____ to curl her hair.

3. The barn _____ when it burst into flames.

4. My mom said to _____ or we will be late.

5. A little green _____ sat in the pond.

turn
turned
turning
curling
curley
curlers

burned
burning
burner

furry
hurry
blurry

purple
gurgle
turtle

1. Thurs day _____   3. mur der _____   5. fur ther _____

2. bur ger _____   4. fur nish _____   6. bur den _____

1. Is Thursday a month? _____   6. Do dogs purr? _____

2. Can a man turn into a bird? _____   7. Can you burn a burger? _____

3. Do turkeys go to church? _____   8. Are girls purple? _____

4. Can girls have curls? _____   9. Do turtles have fur? _____

5. Can turtles jump hurdles? _____   10. Is Thursday a day? _____

64

""*Write the sentences I say.*"

(Introducing the o͞o sound)

"Let's say the picture words together. Underline the pattern as you say the word."

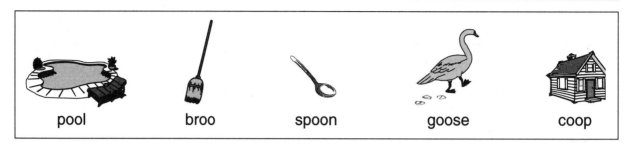

pool   broo   spoon   goose   coop

fool		soon
cool		noon
pool		moon
stool		spoon
spool		
school		

"Write the letter(s) to make it say. . . ."

1. ___ oo   5. ___ ___ oo ___

2. ___ oo ___   6. ___ oo ___

3. ___ ___ oo ___   7. ___ ___ oo ___

4. ___ oo ___   8. ___ oo ___ ___

boo	food
zoo	mood
too	
shoo	

"Write the pattern to make it say. . . ."

1. f_____   5. sw_____

2. s_____   6. b_____

3. br_____   7. ch_____

4. sch_____   8. sp_____

room	toot
zoom	root
loom	hoot
doom	shoot
bloom	

"Write the whole word. . ."

1. _____   4. _____

2. _____   5. _____

3. _____   6. _____

tooth	coop
booth	loop
	hoop
	troop
	droop
	snoop
	swoop
	scoop

roof	loose
goof	moose
proof	goose
	choose

66

(Adding second syllables to o͞o words)

"Next to number 1 write the word. . . ." (snoop)
Next to number 2 write the word. . . ." (snoopy) etc.

1. _____   5. _____   9. _____

2. _____   6. _____   10. _____

3. _____   7. _____   11. _____

4. _____   8. _____   12. _____

"Match the little words to make a compound word."   *"Match the word parts to make a new word."*

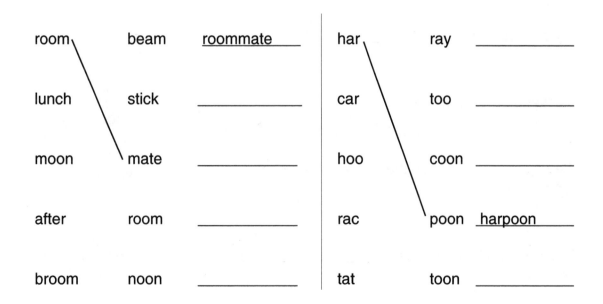

room	beam	roommate
lunch	stick	_____
moon	mate	_____
after	room	_____
broom	noon	_____

har	ray	_____
car	too	_____
hoo	coon	_____
rac	poon	harpoon
tat	toon	_____

(The other sound of **OO** says ŏŏ)			New word	**Live live**

"In the following words the sound is
one you hear in **look** and **good**."

good	look	hook	wool	wollen
wood	book	shook		wooden
hood	cook	brook	woof	
stood	took	crook	hoof	crooked

"Choose the word that makes sense in the sentence.

1. Dad gets very mad when we act _____ .

fooling
fooled
foolish

2. Noodles are good _____ .

doodles
poodles
food

3. They are easy to _____ .

cook
shook
book

4. Snoopy shook his _____ tooth.

loose
moose
goose

5. Chicken and roosters live in _____ .

rooms
pools
coops

6. We _____ on the corner and waited
   for the bus.

stoop
stood
stool

7. Baboons and racoons and _____ live
   in zoos.

tattoos
cartoons
kangaroos

8. I use a broom with a _____ handle to
   clean my room.

wooden
woolen
cooking

68

(A fourth sound for the letter **A**, the sound it often makes with an **L**, as in the word **all**)

"Let's say the picture words together."

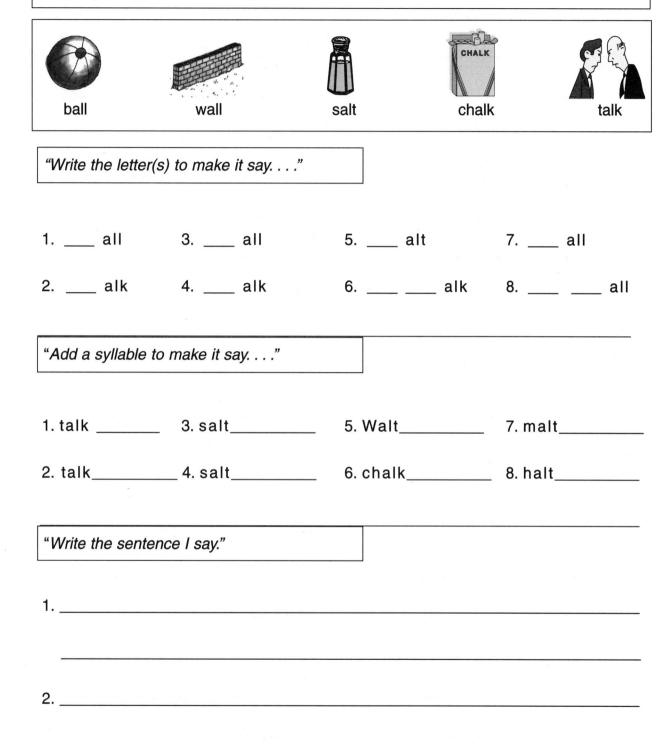

ball   wall   salt   chalk   talk

"Write the letter(s) to make it say. . . ."

1. ____ all   3. ____ all   5. ____ alt   7. ____ all

2. ____ alk   4. ____ alk   6. ____ ____ alk   8. ____ ____ all

"Add a syllable to make it say. . . ."

1. talk _____   3. salt _____   5. Walt _____   7. malt _____

2. talk _____   4. salt _____   6. chalk _____   8. halt _____

"Write the sentence I say."

1. _____

_____

2. _____

_____

Review Test

1. _____
2. _____
3. _____
4. _____
5. _____
6. _____
7. _____
8. _____
9. _____
10. _____
11. _____
12. _____
13. _____
14. _____
15. _____
16. _____
17. _____
18. _____
19. _____
20. _____

21. _____
22. _____
23. _____
24. _____
25. _____
26. _____
27. _____
28. _____
29. _____
30. _____
31. _____
32. _____
33. _____
34. _____
35. _____
36. _____
37. _____
38. _____
39. _____
40. _____